baby
einstein®

Nature

The WALT DISNEP Company

Photo Credits:
Sunset Over Sea, Algave, Portugal © C.B. Knight/Getty Images/FPG • *Floating Maple Leaves*
© PhotoLink/Getty Images/PhotoDisc • *Icicles on Roof of Building* © Richard Price/Getty
Images/Stone • *Sparrows*, Central Park N.Y.C. © Rudi Von Briel/#460947

Visit www.hyperionbooksforchildren.com and www.babyeinstein.com

Great Minds Start Little.™

It's a fine spring day. Violet is exploring.
Today she uses her binoculars.

The binoculars make everything look close and big.
Violet is looking for birds.

Look around. What does Violet see?

Violet sees three sparrows hopping along the riverbed.
The sparrows chirp to one another in little bursts.
They shake and ruffle their brown feathers.
Violet wishes she could hold a sparrow in her hand.

Violet takes a picture.

Look around. What does Violet see?

Violet sees the waves of the ocean.
They move back and forth across the sand.
The waves make the sand wet.
Violet squeezes the wet sand between her toes.
It feels squishy.

The sand is all around her, under the sea, and up the beach in every direction.

What does Violet do?

Violet fills her bucket with water.
The water makes her bucket heavy.
She wiggles her fingers around in the water like little fish.
She touches one wet finger to her tongue.
The water tastes salty.

Sunshine sparkles on the waves of the sea, like little stars.
Violet takes a picture.

Look around. What does Violet see?

Violet sees a leaf.
It floats like a boat along a river of rain
beside the street curb.
There are beautiful raindrops on the leaf.
They glisten like little stars.
Violet takes a picture
and skips along, humming.

The rain slows down.

A big puddle! The biggest puddle ever.
Violet sees the wide sky reflected in the puddle.
She sees the wisps of clouds reflected in the puddle.
Violet sees how flat the top of the puddle is—like glass.

Look around. What does Violet see?

Violet sees icicles hanging from the edge of a roof.
The icicles are clear and bright, like glass.
Violet thinks the icicles are beautiful.
Violet takes a picture.

The snow falls all around.

What does Violet do?

Violet carves a smile on a snowman's face with her finger.
She catches a falling snowflake on her mitten.
When she looks at it closely, Violet sees its pretty design.
Can you count the points on this snowflake?

Sparkling waves

A pretty leaf

Shiny icicles

Three sparrows

Look at all my pictures
from nature!